THE IQ

BOOSTER

Improve your
IQ Performance
Dramatically

ERWIN BRECHER

LIMITED EDITIONS
BOOKTITLES

This edition published for Limited Editions in 1996
1 3 5 7 9 10 8 6 4 2

Edited by Emma Callery
Designed by Jerry Goldie
Cover designed by Nigel Partridge

First published in the United Kingdom in 1996
by Ebury Press
Random House, 20 Vauxhall Bridge Road,
London SW1V 2SA

Random House Australia (Pty) Limited
20 Alfred Street, Milson's Point, Sydney,
New South Wales, 2061, Australia

Random House New Zealand Limited
18 Poland Road, Glenfield, Auckland 10, New Zealand

Random House South Africa (Pty) Limited
PO Box 337, Bergvlei, South Africa

Random House UK Limited Reg. No. 954009

A CIP catalogue record for this book is available from the
British Library

ISBN 0 09 181 229 1

Printed in Great Britain by BPC Hazells Limited,
Aylesbury, Bucks

THE

IQ

BOOSTER

About the Author

Erwin Brecher was born in Budapest and studied mathematics, physics, engineering and psychology in Vienna, Brno (Czechoslovakia), and London. He joined the Czech army in 1938 and after the Nazi occupation of Sudatenland, he escaped to England. Engaged in aircraft design during the War, he later entered the banking profession from which he retired in 1984. Currently, Erwin Brecher devotes his time to playing bridge and chess, and to writing books on scientific subjects or of puzzles, such as *Lateral Logic Puzzles* and *Surprising Science Puzzles* which encompass several of his interests.

A Member of Mensa, Erwin Brecher and his wife, Ellen, make their home in London, England. In 1995, the Viennese Regional Government bestowed the order of Merit in Gold of the City of Vienna on Erwin Brecher, in appreciation of his great achievements.

By the same author:
Journey Through Puzzleland
Lateral Logic Puzzles
Surprising Science Puzzles
Strange Situations
A Puzzle Pot-Pourri

CONTENTS

ACKNOWLEDGEMENTS

I am indebted to:
Victor Serebriakoff
Professor Hans Eysenck
Eamonn Butler and Madsen Pirie
Phillip J Carter and Ken A Russell
for their generosity in letting me use some material
from their books on IQ testing.
I must also thank Leslie Smith and Jennifer Iles for coping
efficiently with the logistics of finalising the manuscript.

INTRODUCTION

There are many classifications which can be applied to the world's population. For the purpose of this book, I would like to divide humanity into Thinkers, Doers and Watchers. Scientific, technical and cultural progress depends on men and women who possess intellectual and artistic faculties, and use them for the advancement of mankind in their respective fields – the Thinkers. The Doers contribute to human progress by using their skills to make the thinkers' dreams and aspirations become reality. The Watchers are passive observers of life as it passes them by, making no attempt at controlling events as they unfold. This may be something of an oversimplification but, in fact, you will find that most people will fit into one of these three broad categories. There may be some overlap: Thinkers can also be Doers, or the other way around; but Watchers will hardly ever take on the guise of Thinkers.

It is at this point that I should declare my colours, anticipating a concerted attack by those who believe that genetics play no– or a negligible – role in intellectual performance; that intellect is wholly or primarily a reflection of external, environmental stimuli. One author describes the view that the genetic ingredient is, by definition, unalterable as "utter and arrogant nonsense". This author's perspective lies at the root of the muddled thinking which pervades this particular discipline of psychology. As analogy he quotes the different IQ test results of a young, unemployed and hungry man compared with his performance when well fed and enjoying financial security. It would take a treatise to prove the fallacy of this argument.

However, to revert to my somewhat arbitrary classification of mankind, not for a moment do I intend to suggest that a person's station in life or relationship to the world around us is genetically programmed. I am merely saying that genetics is one of the factors which determine the path we tread.

Technological developments and progress in the entertainment industry over the last few decades have resulted in a social environment which encourages watching to the detriment of intellectual pursuits. Yet what really counts in the competitive world of today is the ability to deal effectively with the many problems confronting us in our daily lives.

The mental equipment needed to be successful in any field of human endeavour is knowledge and intelligence. There is no mystery about the former. The more you learn and retain in memory, the more you will know. Intelligence in the widest sense is another matter. It is a highly controversial subject, though most scientific opinion agrees that this concept (also referred to as cognitive ability) has an important genetic element. Indeed, it is advisable – to avoid confusion over terminology – to restrict the use of the word 'intelligence' to the genetic contribution to intellectual performance.

An important position in all scientific disciplines is occupied by measurement techniques. The study of measuring cognitive ability is called psychometrics, and the tools used are IQ tests (defined and explained in chapter one). In spite of their many imperfections, such tests have become an important instrument in assessing and evaluating the powers of judgement, comprehension and reasoning of the test subject.

Accepting the premise of a genetic factor, one might assume that IQ test results are a fixed quantum, specific to each individual. This is not so, for three reasons:

● test batteries are not sufficiently standardised to correlate perfectly;
● contrary to scientific imperatives, IQ tests rely to some extent, and in various degrees, on acquired knowledge;
● while genetics in the short and medium term is impervious to extraneous influences, a technique to improve IQ test results can be acquired.

The purpose of this book is two-fold. It will introduce you to the highly emotive and controversial subject of intelligence and the nature-nurture polemic which has been debated with increasing ferocity over many years, a battle which is likely never to subside. The second, and main, purpose is to show how you can improve your test performance by acquainting you with techniques that will have a profound effect on your IQ score, as explained in chapter two. The benefit will exceed by far the eight points generally attributed to test sophistication (see pages 21-2). Indeed, it would not be an exaggeration to say that The IQ Booster could have a far-reaching influence on your future.

Chapter One

WHAT IS INTELLIGENCE?

During his first campaign against Eisenhower, Adlai Stevenson was approached by an enthusiastic supporter: "Governor, every intelligent person will be voting for you." "That's not enough," replied Stevenson; "I need a majority."

Many puzzle and all IQ books deal with the topic of intelligence in their introductions. This is not surprising, as intelligence is the equipment which enables us first to understand, and then to solve, problems. Intelligence testing, and indeed the whole field of mental aptitudes, has been the subject of intense study and research for more than a hundred years, without resulting in a credible consensus among researchers. All of us must have pondered from time to time this elusive faculty with which we are presumably endowed, but which serves some better than others, though some will argue that intelligence is substantially acquired rather than inherited, and this divergence of opinion lies at the heart of the nature-nurture argument.

The word 'intelligence' was coined by Cicero in the form of Inter-Legencia (as an almost literal translation of Aristotle's term Dia-Noesis). Surprisingly, however, for all the academic interest and voluminous literature which the concept of intelligence has attracted, experts have found it difficult even to agree on a definition of the word.

Intelligence has been described as:

"... an innate quality, as distinct from abilities acquired through learning."

(Herbert Spencer)

"... the ability to carry out abstract thinking."

(L M Terman)

"Capacity to act purposefully, think rationally and deal effectively with the environment."

(D Wechsler)

"Innate general cognitive ability."

(Cyril Burt)

"An inborn or innate quality, as distinct from abilities acquired through individual experience ..."

(Encyclopedia Britannica)

While these definitions are not entirely identical, they can at least be reconciled, inasmuch as they do not contradict the view that intelligence is an innate characteristic, specific to each individual.

Another school of thought propagates the view that intelligence is affected to an indeterminate extent by environmental conditions. Some researchers believe that these factors can make the IQ fluctuate by up to 15 points either way. Win Wengers, in his book *How to Increase Your Intelligence*, expresses the opinion that intelligence is eighty percent inherited and twenty percent the result of environmental influences, a view shared by the American psychologist Arthur Jensen. Aside from the question of ratio, it may be thought that the view expressed by Wengers and Jensen simply endorses the general statement that intelligence has a genetic element. But there is a difference. Wengers and Jensen consider the faculty of intelligence itself to be an hereditary and environmental cocktail, while those quoted previously look upon the word 'intelligence' as the genetic contribution towards general intellectual performance. Still other researchers view the concept as being largely a product of environmental influences in the widest sense.

So do we use the term 'intelligence' to mean 'genetic potential', or as a concept consisting of two elements? Or even, in the extreme, is it a product of environmental influence only? For the purpose of this book, I would like to accept Sir Cyril Burt's definition of intelligence as being an "innate general cognitive ability". Cognition is a broad term, but in this context it should stand for reasoning. This negates Wenger's view that intelligence can be increased.

The fact that psychologists, and particularly psychometricians, cannot agree on a definition of intelligence is astonishing. We are not speaking of mere semantics, this divergence of opinions must affect the nature, construction and interpretation of intelligence tests. The literature on this subject is vast and extremely controversial (the nature–nurture polemic). Fortunately, we do not need to join battle, as all we are concerned with in this book is to improve your performance when taking IQ tests, irrespective of what these tests actually measure.

Chapter Two

WHAT YOU SHOULD KNOW ABOUT IQ TESTS

IQ stands for 'intelligence quotient' and is represented by a number. Ideally, this should indicate whether, and to what extent, the intelligence you were born with ranks above or below the average of the population in the cultural entity to which you belong.

As indicated in the introduction, in line with majority scientific opinion, we have to accept that we are not all born equal. This seems self-evident, as if you look around you will see many variations in the colour of eyes, hair and skin, and variances in height and body-build, though it would be a grave mistake to attach any value judgement to these differences. Any one of these traits must be accepted as an accident of birth, and all that distinguishes them is that they are different.

It follows logically that the physical variances extend also to what can be loosely described as talents, which could be artistic or intellectual. Artistic talent finds its expression in works of art, while the level of intellectual talent, generally called intelligence, determines your ability to deal effectively with the many problems you will have to face throughout your life.

It comes as no surprise that much effort has been devoted to finding methods which would make it possible to assess this ability as reliably as possible. Early attempts at intelligence testing go back to the Chinese Mandarin society, and continue throughout the ages until, at the beginning of the twentieth century, Alfred Binet, a Frenchman, succeeded in constructing tests which were used by the French educational system to identify children who did not achieve the required grade.

The concept of intelligence quotient (IQ) was born after Binet was translated into English at Stanford University in the USA. By definition:

$$IQ = \frac{MA}{CA} \times 100$$

whereby MA stands for Mental Age, CA for Chronological Age, and the factor 100 is used to eliminate decimals.

For the purpose of IQ tests, it is assumed that the average IQ in the society in which you live is 100. Thus, if you are 10 years old (CA) and you pass tests which most 10-year-olds will pass, you are said to have a Mental Age (MA) of 10. Then:

$$\frac{MA}{CA} \times 100 = \frac{10}{10} \times 100 = 100$$

If you pass the same test at the age of 8, then:

$$\frac{MA}{CA} \times 100 = \frac{10}{8} \times 100 = 125$$

Therefore your IQ is 125, well above average. Conversely, if you cannot pass this test until you reach the age of 12 then your IQ is 83.33.

At this point you should realise that the above is a simplified version of a very complicated and controversial subject, on which a huge bibliography has been generated by researchers. To avoid confusion, it should be said that the scales and tests have been modified often since Binet (notably by L Terman of Stanford University, whose work gave rise to the Stanford–Binet Test). In time, it became clear that the MA/CA x 100 formula could not apply once chronological age arrived at maturity (the result would be a progressive apparent deterioration in IQ). So by way of correction the Wechsler Adult Intelligence Scale (WAIS) was devised by David Wechsler in 1944.

As said before, IQ tests are designed to establish whether, and to what extent, you perform above or below average in intelligence tests. However, IQ tests have one major flaw. It is virtually impossible to construct tests that will assess the intelligence you were born with irrespective of any knowledge you might have acquired as part of your education. For one thing, you need a basic knowledge of the test language – sufficient to understand the question and to have a sense for the meaning of words and their relationship to each other.

Psychometricians constructing IQ tests should avoid making demands on an advanced vocabulary which is not a measure of the innate faculty the tests are presumed to assess. Surprisingly, most so-called intelligence tests disregard this basic principle. The result disadvantages the intelligent in favour of the well-educated.

Victor Serebriakoff, honourary president of International Mensa, formulates: "A well-designed intelligence test should not, of course, test the educational background of the subject. Even the verbal test items are usually chosen to avoid those items (questions) where the answers would be more likely to be known to a well-educated person. It is the ability of the subject to discern the exact shade of meaning of relatively common words which is measured, and not his knowledge of esoteric ones like 'esoteric'."

This is a most important qualification which, unfortunately, is not observed by many test designers. Professor Hans Eysenck articulates the same point even more succinctly: "… intelligence tests do not measure innate capacity or potential; the most that can be said is that they suggest estimates of innate capacity …" In the arena of mental ability tests, the principle of 'horses for courses' should apply.

IQ tests should target the genetic component. Instead, they mostly test intellectual performance, which is a function of innate intelligence applied to acquired knowledge and experience. Competence assessment tests should be designed to evaluate intellectual performance with specialisation in a specific field. In practical terms, both ingredients – intelligence and education – are needed to cope effectively with the demands of life.

An Australian Aborigine can be very intelligent, but if he has had no education he will perform badly in civilised society. Equally, a person whose intelligence is below average but who has enjoyed an excellent education will not be able to apply the academic level which he has reached to best effect.

Regrettably, constructing IQ tests that measure the genetic component of intellectual performance is only a pipe dream. As they are constructed, they measure a composite faculty consisting of innate intelligence and acquired knowledge (culture contamination). To design completely culture-free test material is impossible. The best we can hope for are tests that are as culture-fair as possible.

What is meant by culture-free tests can best be demonstrated by the classic Koehler experiment. The German psychologist Wolfgang Koehler (1887-1967), working with a number of chimpanzees, gave each of them two hollow sticks which singly were too short to reach a banana outside the cage. One of the chimpanzees was observed mulling over the problem and, after a little thought, fitting two sticks together providing a tool to reach the banana. This achievement was the result of genetic intelligence (nature) pure and simple, as the environment (nurture) could have played no part in the problem's solution.

There are several high-IQ organisations, of which Mensa, founded in 1946 in Oxford, England, is the best known. It has by now almost 100,000 members worldwide. Mensa admits as members, individuals who pass a supervised IQ test and score in the top two percent of the population.

This book (or any other) cannot teach you to be intelligent. It will, however, help you to use the mental equipment you were born with to best advantage. At one time or another you will most likely come across IQ tests, and if so, you will meet many of the problems in this book and greet them as old friends.

There are three groups of tests constituting what is referred to as a 'test battery':

Verbal

Linked to knowledge of language and understanding of the meaning of words.

Numerical

Linked to numbers and their relationships to each other.

Visuo-spatial

Dealing with objects, signs, symbols and illustrations.

These groups are designed to test different mental abilities, though it is accepted that if you are good at one you are usually good at all three of them.

Here are some examples of each group using analogies. These are offered on the assumption that some readers might be unfamiliar with the subject. To those who consider these explanations somewhat elementary, I apologise.

Verbal

SHORT is to LONG as BLACK is to:
Low Green Far White

Your answer will, of course, be white.

If you did not know what analogy was, this example will have shown you. A proper definition would be: "A comparison of two pairs, whereby the relationship of the two elements of the second pair is the same as that of the first pair."

Numerical

2 is to 4 as 4 is to: 16, 30, 8, 12.

The answer is clearly 8.

Visuo-spatial

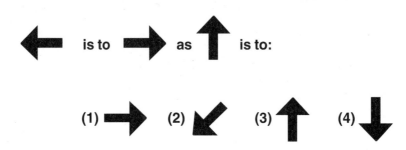

The answer is 4.

These problems were all analogies, but there are many other types of test questions which can be used with each group. In the course of the Before Test (see pages 23-41) you will meet several other types.

Your rating

Results from these tests can be combined to produce a single score which determines your IQ rating. In chapter five I give you several examples of each type of test and show you how to tackle them. You will soon find your test scores getting progressively better until you have acquired a technique which will give you a decisive edge over others who have not read this book. This technique is called test sophistication, and is the subject of the next chapter.

Chapter Three

TEST SOPHISTICATION

(or how to improve your performance in intelligence tests)

IQ tests, in a wide variety, have become an integral part of academic and professional competence assessment. Test sophistication is defined as the extent to which a person has had experience with IQ tests, and therefore is aware of the general nature of these tests and has acquired a technique which will give such test-wise individuals an advantage over those who are unfamiliar with the subject.

Some researchers estimate that this head start could be worth as much as eight points in test results. I believe that, given the right training, this is an underestimate and could be worth considerably more. This book sets out to familiarise the reader with techniques which will achieve the desired result. Indeed, it will do more than acquaint you with typical IQ test questions as other books on the subject do. It aims to channel your thought processes towards a discipline that will reduce confusion and time-consuming trial-and-error efforts, with a commensurate benefit beyond the scope of this book. The extent to which this objective will be achieved can be accurately measured in the comparison between the Before Test (pages 23-51) and After Test (pages 78-125) results.

The phenomenon of test sophistication seems, at first glance, to contradict our view that the innate element of intelligence cannot be enhanced by acquired know-how. It should not be thought of as an exercise akin to training for a four-minute mile which actually improves your speed. Getting acquainted with IQ tests is more in the nature of acquiring improved dexterity in the use of a tool, without widening the range of applications for which the tool is designed. By way of analogy, assume that you would like to trim your hedge using ordinary garden shears. If you have never tried before you will do a mediocre job, probably taking longer than you should, and the edges will not be as straight as you would have hoped. If, on the other hand, you have been trained in the use of the tool, you will do a better job in half the time. However, and this is the relevant point, you will never be able to cut your cuticles with the shears.

In summary, chapter five of this book is designed to do two things:
● To familiarise you with the full range of test questions in general use.
● To show you how to approach the task of finding the correct answer systematically and competently.

After you have read this book, you should be a fully-fledged TEST SOPHISTICATE. The before-and-after exercise will show how much you have benefitted from this book. The Before Test on pages 23-51 consists of twenty tests in each group – verbal, numerical and visuo-spatial – together with answers. Follow the instructions carefully and compare your test score as directed for comparison with the After Test result.

Chapter Four

THE BEFORE TEST

General directions

- You have 50 minutes to complete all 60 questions.
- Answer the questions as carefully and as quickly as you can.
- Begin at the beginning and go straight through.
- Don't give up easily, but if you have no clue move to the next question. You can always go back if you have time to spare.
- It is advisable to write your answers on a separate piece of paper so that the book can be used again.
- If you think you might have the right answer, note it down even if you are not quite certain.
- Do not exceed the time limit.
- If you are one of the few who has never seen an IQ test, you will probably find the Before Test difficult. Do not be discouraged; you will do much better in the After Test which, after all, is the purpose of this book.

BEFORE TEST QUESTIONS

VERBAL

Elimination

Find the one word which does not fit in with the others, either as to meaning or construction.

1 Walked   Rode   Sailed   Travelled   Flew

2 Educate   Explain   Instruct   Teach   Train

3 Warm   Tepid   Cold   Heat   Freezing

4 Thirst   Defrost   Relax   Hijack   Student

5 Doodle   Entreat   Memorise   Exchange   Remorse

Analogies

Identify the word that completes the analogy.

6 VEIL is to CURTAIN as EYE is to:

   VIEW   SEE   WINDOW   EYELID   TEARS

7 TRAM is to MART as PART is to:

   TRIM   START   STOP   TRAP   PORT

8 DESTRUCTIONS is to TOTE as REPRODUCTION is to:

   RUIN   TUTOR   NEST   RICE   COIN

Hint: the answers to 7 and 8 lie not in the meaning of the words.

Find the word that fits

Find the word in the second line that will fit best into the first line:

9 Division   Marine   Contract   Tenant

Addition   Agreement   Country   Title   Storm

Missing word

Insert the four-letter word missing in the lower brackets.

10 POLICEMAN   (MARS)   NURSE

  SOLICITOR   (. . . .)   BARRISTER

11 WORKER   (ROAM)   AMAZE

  TESTER   (. . . .)   OMEN

12 GRID   (RING)   HANG

  STIR   (. . . .)   GAFF

Alphabet problems

13 Insert the next letter in the sequence.

O   T   F   S   N   E   T   F   S   N   T   T   ?

Here is a letter square:

See how the letters are arranged. Thus P comes just after O. T is just below O. P is between K and U. Now answer these questions:

A	B	C	D	E
F	G	H	J	K
L	M	N	O	P
Q	R	S	T	U
V	W	X	Y	Z

14 Find the letter that comes between the letter between A and L and the letter between N and X.

15 Find the letter that comes just before the letter just above the letter between M and O.

16 Find the letter that comes just after the letter that comes just above the letter just before the letter just above N.

17 Find the letter that comes just above the letter which comes just after the letter which comes between the letter just above N and the letter just below L.

18 Find the letter that comes just below the letter which comes between the letter just after the letter just above F and the letter just before the letter just below K.

Identification

19 Insert the letter K above or below the line.

A				E	F		H	I	
	B	C	D			G			J

20 Identify the word which is nearest in meaning to the word

DIFFERENT:
Irregular   Abnormal   Unlike   Strange   Unusual

NUMERICAL

Series

A series is a sequence of numbers which follows a specific pattern.

Insert the missing number(s).

21 1   3   5   6   7   9   11   12   ?

22 2   5   10   17   26   ?

23 ?   7   10   13   16

24 6   7   9   ?   16   21

25 5   6   7   8   10   11   14   ?   ?

26 5   ?   7   11   10   8   14   6   ?

27 1   2   5   10   17   ?

28

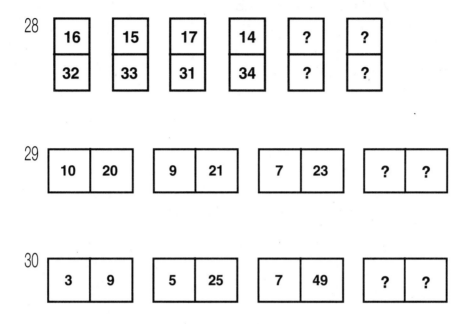

16	15	17	14	?	?
32	33	31	34	?	?

29

| 10 | 20 | | 9 | 21 | | 7 | 23 | | ? | ? |

30

| 3 | 9 | | 5 | 25 | | 7 | 49 | | ? | ? |

Analogies

31 If ²/₃ is 4, how much is 3?

Completion

In each set of missiles there are rules which allow the target number of the missile to be formed from the numbers in the tail and wings. In the example, the rule is: add the wing numbers and multiply by the tail numbers to get the target number.

Example

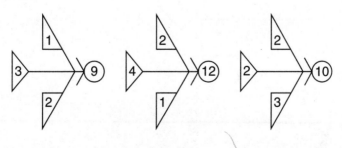

Insert the missing numbers.

32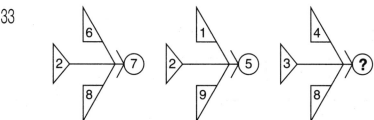

33

34 Insert the missing number in the empty space so that the third illustration follows the same rule as the first two.

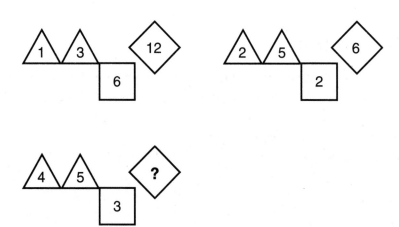

35 Insert the missing number using the same arithmetical operation as the first line.

12   (54)   15

21   (??)   13

Insert the missing number.

36

15	23	4
6	?	11
5	19	7

37

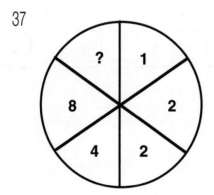

38

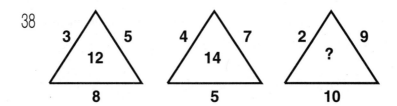

39

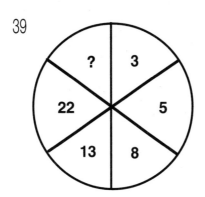

40

10		1		15		3		12		2
	8				49				?	
8		3		8		4		6		4

VISUO-SPATIAL

Selection

41 Select the correct figure from the five numbered ones.

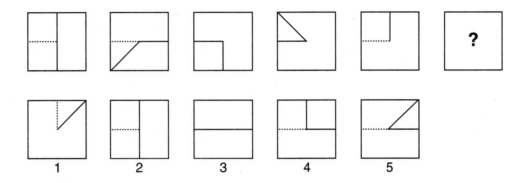

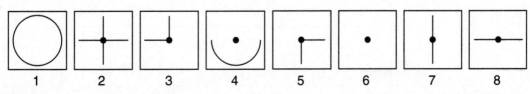

42 Select the correct figure
from the eight numbered ones.

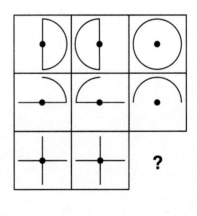

43 Select the correct
figure from the six
numbered ones.

44 Select the correct
figure from the six
numbered ones.

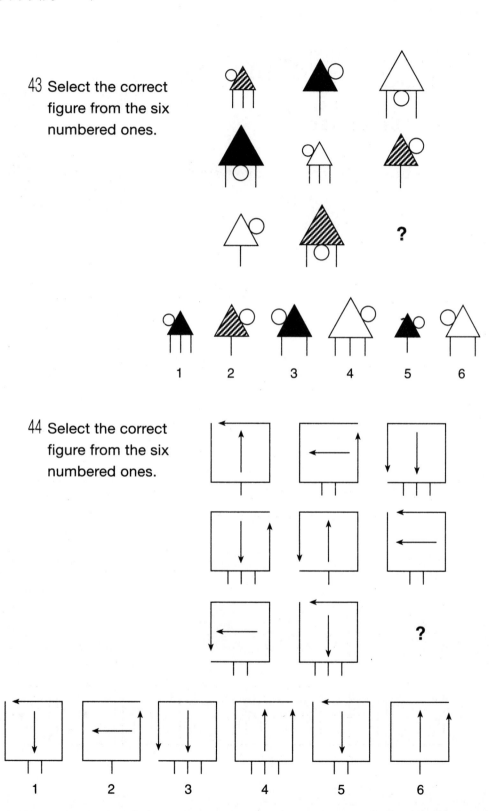

45 Select the correct
figure from the six
numbered ones.

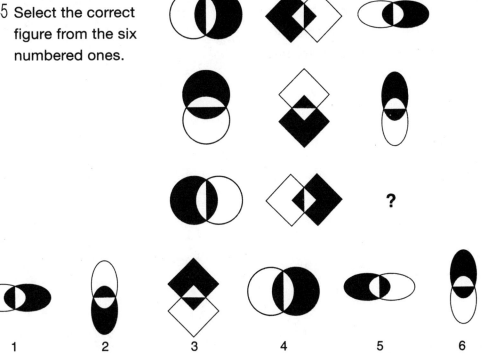

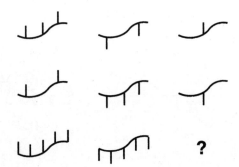

1   2   3   4   5   6

46 Select the correct
figure from the five
numbered ones.

?

1   2   3   4   5

47 Select the correct
fish from the five
numbered ones.

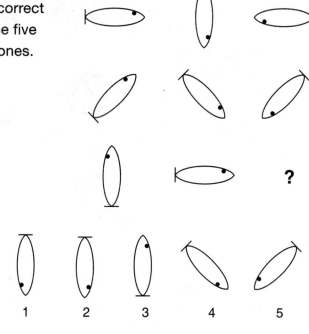

?

1   2   3   4   5

48 Select the correct
figure from the six
numbered ones.

?

1   2   3   4   5   6

Odd man out

49 Find the odd man out.

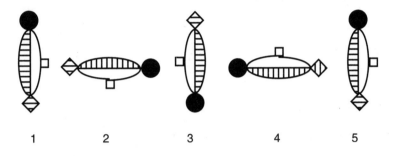

1   2   3   4   5

50 Find the odd man out.

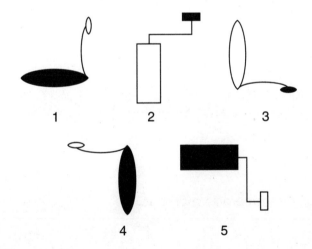

51 Find the odd man out.

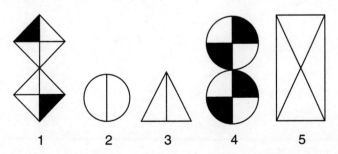

1   2   3   4   5

52 Find the odd man out.

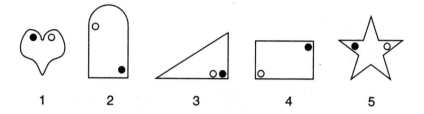

1	2	3	4	5

53 Find the three odd men out.

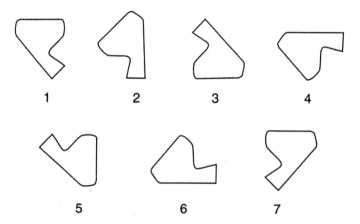

54 Find the three odd men out.

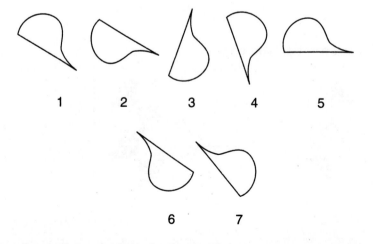

55 Find the two odd men out.

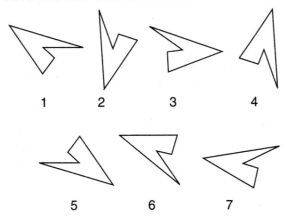

1   2   3   4

5   6   7

56 Find the odd man out.

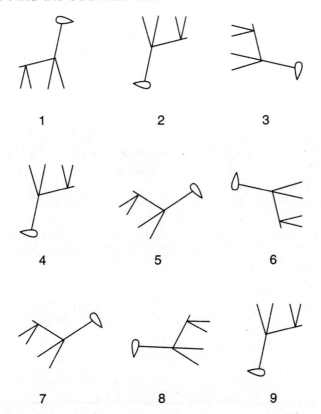

1   2   3

4   5   6

7   8   9

Analogies

57 Find the figure that completes the analogy.

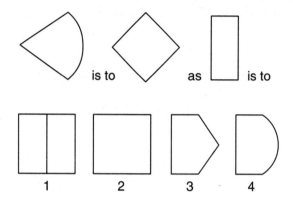

is to   as   is to

| 1 | 2 | 3 | 4 |

58 Find the figure that completes the analogy without turning over.

is to   as   is to

| | 1 | 2 | 3 | 4 |

Series

59 Draw the domino that completes the series.

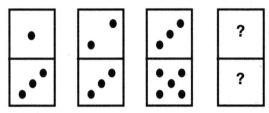

60 Select the figure that completes the series.

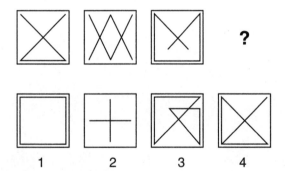

BEFORE TEST ANSWERS

1 Travelled.

(The others are specific ways of travelling.)

2 Explain.

(All the others imply a teacher–student relationship.)

3 Heat.

(All the others refer to temperature. Heat is energy. Also, heat is the only noun; the other words are adjectives.)

4 Relax.

(All the others contain three letters in alphabetical order: RST, DEF, HIJ, STU.)

5 Exchange.

(All the other words contain two vowels and two consonants which are identical.)

6 WINDOW.

(A veil covers the eyes but is detachable; curtains cover windows and are also detachable.)

7 TRAP.

(TRAP is PART back to front, as are TRAM and MART.)

8 RICE.

(TOTE is composed of the fourth, tenth, eighth and second letters of DESTRUCTIONS. The same applies to RICE and REPRO-DUCTION.)

9 Title.

(All the words in the top row can be prefixed with SUB to give another word, as does Title.)

10 TOTE.

(The first two letters of MARS are the same as the last two letters but one of POLICEMAN and the last two letters of MARS are the same as the last two letters but one of NURSE.
Using the same principle with SOLICITOR and BARRISTER, we get TOTE.)

11 SEEM.

(**ROAM – TESTER, ROAM – OMEN**)

12 TIFF.
(**RING** – STIR, **RING** – GAFF)

13 T.
(They are the initial letters of the odd numbers: One, Three, Five, Seven, etc.)

14 M.

15 G.

16 C.

17 H.

18 N.

19 Above the line – like all other straight line letters. Curved letters go below the line.

20 Unlike.

21 13.
(Consecutive numbers are increased as follows:
+2 +2 +1 +1 +2 +2 +1 +1)

22 37.

(Square 1, 2, 3, 4, 5 and 6, and add 1; or increase consecutively by 3, 5, 7, 9, 11)

23 4.

(The difference between the numbers is 3.)

24 12.

(The difference between the numbers grows by one each time.)

25 15, 19.

(This series does not appear to make any sense until you realise that the numbers represent not a single sequence but two, thus:

5	7	10	14	?

and:

6	8	11	?	)

26 19, 15.

(This is, in fact, the same as the question above, except that one sequence goes left to right and the other goes right to left.)

27 26.

(There are two ways of looking at it, both yielding the same answer. Add the sequence of odd numbers:

$1 + 1 = 2, 2 + 3 = 5, 5 + 5 = 10, 10 + 7 = 17, 17 + 9 = 26.$

Alternatively this is just a set of squares of 0, 1, 2, 3, 4 and 5, with 1 added to each.)

28

18	13
30	35

(Each row contains two interlocking series, one in ascending and one in descending order. Incidentally, the numbers also add up to 48.)

29 4 and 26.

(The left numbers progress by subtracting 1, 2, 3. The right numbers increase by 1, 2, 3.)

30 9 and 81.

(The first numbers in successive double squares form a series by adding twos, and the second numbers are the squares of the corresponding first numbers.)

31 18.

($4 = {}^{12}/_3$, ie 6 times ${}^2/_3$, therefore $3 = 18$.)

32 6.

(Add numbers in wings and tail.)

33 4.

(Add numbers in wings and divide the result by the number in the tail.)

34 3.

(Find the difference between the numbers in the triangles, and multiply the result with the number in the square.)

35 68.

(Add the numbers outside the bracket and double the sum.)

36 28.

(The figures in the centre column are obtained by doubling the figures in the last column and adding them to the figure in the first column, ie 2 x 4 + 15 = 23.)

37 32 or 8.

(For the first answer, multiply the first number by the second to get the third: 1 x 2 = 2; then multiply the second and third numbers to get the fourth, and so on. Finally, 4 x 8 = 32. Or, to arrive at 8: numbers on the left are 4 times their opposites.)

38 18.

(Multiply the three numbers outside the triangle and divide by 10.)

39 39.

(Beginning with 3, each number is double the preceding one, minus 1, 2, 3, 4, etc. Thus: 22 x 2 = 44 – 5 = 39.)

40 36.

(The number in the centre box is calculated by adding the right-hand numbers and multiplying the result with the difference between the left-hand numbers. Thus: 1 + 3 = 4 x (10 – 8) = 8.)

41 5.

(There are two black arms – one moves through 90° each time and the other through 45°. The dotted line never moves but is covered by the black arms when they coincide with its position.)

42 6.

(Looking across, the mirror images of the curved lines merge, and straight lines disappear. Looking down, the reverse happens.)

43 1.

(There are three sizes of triangle, three kinds of shading, three different positions for the circle, and either one, two, or three legs. Each of these is only found once in each row or column.)

44 6.

(There are three positions for the arrow inside the square and three positions for the arrow on the outside of the square; there are 1, 2 or 3 supports.)

45 5.

(The figure must consist of 2 horizontal ellipses, with black on the left side.)

46 3.

(Take the lines above the snake to be plus, and the lines below to be minus, and then add up the first two figures in each line to make the third. Thus the second line is +2 –3 = –1, and the last line is +4 –4 = 0.)

47 2.

(The fish move clockwise by one-quarter of a revolution in each row.)

48 3.

(Men count +1, women -1; 2 - 2 = 0.)

49 2.

(All shadings are parallel but in 2 they are at right angles to each other.)

50 4.

(Figures 1 and 3 form a pair, and so do 2 and 5. In each pair one figure has been rotated through 90 degrees, and the black and white shading have been interchanged. Figure 4 does not fit into this.)

51 3.

(All others appear the same turned upside down.)

52 3.

(Each can be divided symmetrically, with a dot in each half, except 3.)

53 1, 3 and 6.

(The other four can be rotated into each other.)

54 2, 3 and 7.

(The other four can be rotated into each other.)

55 3 and 6.

(The other figures can be rotated into each other.)

56 8.

(All the other figures can be rotated into each other.)

57 2.

(Remove the right–hand edge and replace it with a mirror-image of the remainder.)

58 2.

(The letter N is turned 180° and becomes a mirror image and therefore stays the same.)

59

(The lower dots represent the number of letters of the top dots.)

60 3.

(The number of lines increases by one each time. There is no other pattern.)

HOW TO SCORE

To be counted as correct, your answers must conform precisely to the Before Test key. For each correct answer, score 2 points.

To find your IQ, enter your score on the horizontal line of the graph below. Draw a vertical line until it meets the diagonal line at P. From P draw a horizontal line until it meets the vertical line pinpointing your IQ. The example given indicates that if you answer 40 questions (80 points) your IQ rating is about 127, well above the average (100).

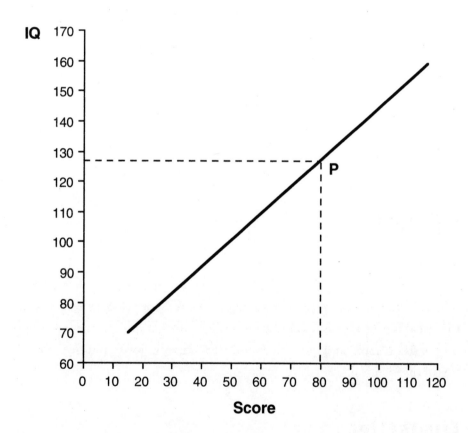

Warning: neither the Before Test nor the After Test is validated and/or standardised. However, they would correlate reasonably well with standard IQ tests. At any rate, our main interest lies in comparing before and after results.

Chapter Five

ACQUIRING TECHNIQUE

In this chapter we shall learn to understand the nature of test questions and the systematic methods that will lead to correct answers without wasting time with 'trial-and-error' efforts. Lessons are also drawn from the Before Test, and specific questions are referred to, adding the prefix BT to the question number.

VERBAL

This test group is, by its very nature, the least likely to be culture-fair. Even if one avoids the need for an advanced vocabulary, it demands from the test subject somewhat more than basic English. A feel for subtle differences in the meaning of words, that appear to be synonymous, is needed. The meanings of 'walk' and 'go', 'freedom' and 'liberty', 'look' and 'see' are by no means identical.

Elimination

● You are given five or six words, of which all but one have something in common.

Find the one which does not belong:
Lion   Tiger   Elephant   Horse   Canary   Zebra

Solution This is easy: canary is a bird and all the others are mammals.

● A little more difficult:

Hope Love Affection Envy Admiration

Solution Envy.
(All the other words are positive emotions.)

● But watch out for test questions that do not rely on the meanings of words but on their construction:

Engine Othello Noun Animal Madam

With questions like this you will have difficulties in finding the odd man out because of the different principle applied. Once again, don't look for a meaning but for another peculiarity which is common to four of the five words.

Solution Animal.
(All the other words have identical first and last letters.)

● There are many other elimination tests based on word construction, such as:
The number of letters, syllables, vowels and consonants.
The order in which vowels and consonants are used.

● One more example of this type:

Find the odd man out:
First Defunct Patience Hijack Stupid

Solution Patience.
(All the others contain three letters in alphabetical order: RST, DEF, HIJ, STU.) (Also used in BT4 on page 24.)

Analogies

● These were dealt with as examples for the three groups (see pages 19-20), but here are a few more. As with the elimination questions, you have to consider meaning as well as word construction.

HAND is to GLOVE as FOOT is to:

Stocking   Floor   Shoestring   Shoe

Watch it! Would you have said shoe?

Solution Stocking.

CLOCK is to TIME as THERMOMETER is to:
Heat   Fever   Temperature   Humidity

This is somewhat tricky. Think before you answer. I presume that you have eliminated humidity at once. (The instrument for measuring humidity is called a hygrometer.)

Solution Temperature.
(Heat is the energy transferred from a body at a higher temperature to one of a lower temperature. Fever is simply an abnormally high body temperature.)

● One more example where the relationship is not of meaning but of structure:

STAR is to RATS as WARD is to:
Shine   Mice   Draw   Fame

As there is no likely relationship between a Star and Rats, you should be looking for the arrangement of the letters.

Solution Draw.

(Ward read backwards, as is the case with Rats and Star — BT7 on page 25.)

● Unfortunately, verbal analogies are invariably culture-contaminated, to use psychometric jargon, because they demand an understanding of vocabulary which goes beyond basic knowledge of the test language. Take for example the following question that was used in a Mensa test and, in my opinion, is inappropriate:

Manner is to matter as. . . say, frown, custom, word, message.

Solution Message, word.

(The only technique that could be applied here is to use a process of elimination. Frown and custom make no sense whatsoever. So we are left with say, word and message. It could be a toss-up between say and word, except that manner is a noun and therefore we must opt for word.)

Find the word that fits

Another type of verbal test you are likely to meet requires a different mental approach altogether. In fact, this offers a perfect example of the value of test sophistication. If you did not solve BT9 on page 25, once you know the solution, all other tests based on the same principle will present no problem.

● Find the word in the second line which will fit best into the first line:

Ship   Speed   Man   Terminal   Space
Healthy   Insured   Sick   Well   Tired

Solution Sick.

(All the words in the top line can be prefixed with 'Air'. Only with 'Sick' in the second line can you do the same.)

● Now try:

Lady   Lord   Mark   Slide   Mass
Beaten   Locked   Tested   Opened   Closed

Solution Locked.

(You will have guessed that the prefix is Land.)

● So, the way to identify this type of question is to see whether any of the words in the second line will make sense with a prefix or suffix. There are a number of prefixes or suffixes available for such tests:

Back-   -fire,   -gammon,   -ground,   -hand,   -lash,   -log
Under --ground,   -study,   -bid,   -cover,   -dog,   -carriage
Over-   -pass,   -seas,   -hear,   -lap,   -rule,   -night
and other prefixes include: Dia-   Con-   Com-   Inter-   Off-

Missing word

● Insert the word missing from the brackets:

HOUSE   (HEAD)   AGED
BRIDE   (....)   LINT

Solution BELT.

(Having come across this type of test in BT10, BT11 and BT12 on page 26, you will have no problem here.)

● Once again you will agree that knowing the principle involved unlocks all other puzzles of this type. However, you need to be mentally alert because, while the principle remains the same, there are variations. For example, look at:

ARDOUR   (RAIN)   NINETY
OPPRESSION (....)   TRAPPINGS

Solution PORT.

(The second and first letters of each word, in that order.)

● Now one more with a slight twist:

SIMPLETON   (TEST)   STETSON
QUARRY   (....)   WINNING

Solution RAIN.

(The word in brackets is made up of the last but two and last but three letters, in that order, of the word before the brackets, and the same letters of the word after the brackets.)

You may have noticed, of course, that some letters are duplicated giving a multiple choice. In most cases you will quickly recognise which to use. If not, write down the possibilities. In the above example the exercise would yield the following combinations:

RAWI

RAIW

RAWN

RAIN

There can be no doubt about the answer.

● Incidentally, you will find the same principle used in the numerical section!

Alphabet problems

● Which letter logically fills the gap?

A   B   C   D   ?   F

Solution E.

(Nothing could be simpler!)

● However, this type of test can cover a wide range of complexity. Try this, for example, where you need to find the missing letter.

A   D   G   J   ?

Solution M.

(Again in alphabetical order, but after each letter two further letters are missed out.)

● Now for a slightly more difficult one:

A   B   D   G   ?   P

Before you try to find the missing letter, here is an invaluable aid to solving all alphabet problems. Write down the alphabet and number each letter as follows:

A	B	C	D	E	F	G	H	I	J	K	L	M	N	O	P	Q	R	S	T	U	V	W	X	Y	Z
1	2	3	4	5	6	7	8	9	10	11	12	13	14	15	16	17	18	19	20	21	22	23	24	25	26

Using the aid, you will find that the known letters are numbered:

1,   2,   4,   7,   ?,   16.

Consequently, the missing letter must be number 11, equivalent to K.

● Here is BT13 again: What is the next letter is this sequence?

O T F S N E T F S N T T ?

Using the matrix for corresponding numbers to these letters will get you nowhere. As you have seen, these are the initial letters of odd numbers. The lesson you can learn: be prepared for the phonetic approach if nothing else makes sense.

● Can you find the next letter in the following sequence?

T   F   S   E   T   T   F   S   E   T   ?

This should now be easy.

Solution T.

(The first letters of even numbers, starting with Two.)

● Try to solve this, filling in the appropriate letter at the question mark:

ABA   CDC   EFE   G?G   IJI

Solution H.

(Using the aid, you get 121, 343, 565, 787, 9109. Therefore the missing letter must be 8, equivalent to H.)

● Now tackle the letter square used in BT14 to BT18 on page 27.

A	B	C	D	E
F	G	H	J	K
L	M	N	O	P
Q	R	S	T	U
V	W	X	Y	Z

These questions can be confusing unless you adopt a strategy. Take BT17 for example. Starting from the back and working towards the beginning, divide the question into five components as indicated. Then find the letters, step by step:

(5) Find the letter that comes just above (4), the letter that comes just after (3), the letter that comes between (2), the letter just above N (1) and the letter just below L.

1 The letter just below L = Q. Now continue:

2 = H

3 = M

4 = N

5 = H

QED

● So far these tests have called on your problem-solving ability, ie your intelligence. However, there are a great number of verbal tests that assume some specialised knowledge or an extensive vocabulary. These are not proper IQ tests as they offend against the basic principle which should govern all such tests, as explained in chapter one. Here are some examples of flawed test questions:

Which of the following cities is not located in Europe?

London   Budapest   Munich   Tangier   Geneva   Graz

You might find this easy and pick out the correct city. Even so, it is nonsensical to include it in an IQ test. You either know that Tangier is in Africa or you don't. At any rate, it has nothing to do with your intelligence. The question would probably be posed along 'odd man out' lines, but the objection still applies.

Even more obscure are questions making a demand on your vocabulary beyond basic English. A member of MENSA devised this test for the supposedly 'super-intelligent': Which does not belong?

Dada   Abstract   Expressionist   Cubist
Dodecaphonic   Pointillist

Don't give it another thought. This is a problem which belongs in an examination for second-year art students, not in an IQ test. It betrays a lack of understanding on the part of the deviser of the difference between an intelligent person and an academic who has enjoyed specialised education.

Even more extreme would be the following analogy taken from a book dealing with intelligence tests, under the heading 'Match Wits with Mensa':

Roquefort is to France as Liederkranz is to ...

Solution USA.

(Liederkranz is an American cheese named after a singing group organised by a cheese producer of German origin. Armed with that piece of [peripheral] knowledge, any test subject would make

light work of the question; without it, the question is unanswer-
able, however intelligent the subject.)

Identification

● Whether you have or have not guessed the answer to BT19 on page 00,
it is worthwhile to elaborate on this type of test because it is one of the
few which, in psychometric lingo, is entirely culture free. Its proper
place would be in the visuo-spatial section but by locating it where it is,
you are tested for alertness. Such questions can appear in different forms,
such as:

Insert the letter W above or below the line.

Solution Below the line.
(The location depends on a physical characteristic. All letters
below the line are symmetrical about a vertical axis.)

● Following the same principle, another question would be:

Insert the letters S and R above or below the line.

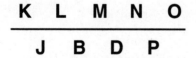

Solution S above, R below the line.
(Straight and curved letters above, mixed straight and curved
below.)

NUMERICAL

The Before Test used series and completions. These and other types are equivalent to the verbal tests, but dressed in arithmetical couture.

Series

A series is a sequence of numbers (mostly integers) which follows a specific, identifiable pattern. The simplest example is:

    1   2   3   4   5   6   7   8   9   ?

Solution 10.

● Needless to say, test questions are more intricate. What do you make of the following?

    1   3   2   4   3   5   4   6   5   7   ?

A useful first step, which is a key to many numerical tests, is to write down the differences between all adjacent numbers, thus:

1 [+2] 3 [-1] 2 [+2] 4 [-1] 3 [+2] 5 [-1] 4 [+2] 6 [-1] 5 [+2] 7 [-1] ?

In this way you will neatly arrive at the answer.

Solution 6.

● There are other ways of considering series. Looking at the above example again it, in fact, consists of two interlinked series:

    1   2   3   4   5   6

      3   4   5   6   7

This idea will recur in many different forms. Try:

2 3 4 6 6 9 8 12 10 15 12 ?

Here differences will make no sense, but two interlinked series will.

Solution 18.
(The two series are 2, 4, 6, 8, 10, 12 and 3, 6, 9, 12, 15.)

● To make these types of questions easier to work out, use the aid of differences between adjacent numbers. In this way, BT23 on page 28 is elementary. However, BT25 and BT26 also on page 28 are more complex. But if you remember that two missing numbers indicate two interlocking series, the answers will then fall into place.

● Here is a further example of two series running together, but in a different form:

1	3	7	15	?
240	48	12	4	?

Solution

(In the top row add 2, 4, 8, 16. In the bottom row start on the right and, beginning with 2, multiply consecutive numbers by 2, 3, 4 and 5.)

Analogies

● Select the correct answer from the line beneath this analogy:

¹/₃ is to 3, as 3 is to ?

6 ¹/₆ 9 12 27

Solution 27.
(3 is 9 times ¹/₃, and 27 is 9 times 3.)

● Working out the above is easy enough but if a fraction is involved a further simplification would be to convert the integer into fractions with the same denominator.

● BT31 is somewhat more difficult as no alternative answers are given.

If $^2/_3$ is 4, how much is 3?

In fractions it can be stated thus:

If $^2/_3$ is $^{12}/_3$, how much is $^9/_3$?

Solution 18.

(The answer must be 6 times as much, namely $^{54}/_3$ or 18.)

● Another technique which might suit some readers better is to use an equation. For example:

If $^7/_8$ is 1 $^3/_4$, how much is 1 $^1/_2$?

In arithmetical terms, this would be:

$^7/_8 : 1\,^3/_4 = 1\,^1/_2 : x$

As an equation, this would be:

$^7/_8\,x = 1\,^3/_4 \times 1\,^1/_2$

Turn it into fractions and simplify:

$$\frac{7x}{8} = \frac{168}{64} = \frac{21}{8}$$

Therefore, $x = 3$

Completion

● The types of completion tests shown at BT32 and BT33 on page 30 are subject to a trial-and-error exercise using arithmetic operations such as divisions, multiplications, subtractions and additions in various combinations. Squares are rarely used. Even so, these tests will often yield to cognitive analysis which will afford a short-cut to the solution. Take for instance the first missile of BT33.

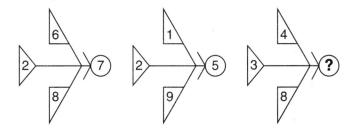

The target number 7 cannot be a product. Neither can it be a sum or a subtraction of even numbers, leaving a division. This reasoning suggests the Solution 'Add the wings and divide by the tail'.

● BT34 on page 30 is constructed on the same principle. It is, however, worth noting that different geometrical figures usually indicate different arithmetic operations.

● Tests in the format of BT32, BT33 and BT34 are standard fare. However, look at this more difficult example:

Insert the missing number.

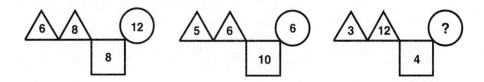

Solution 18.

(Multiply the triangles and divide by half of the square.)

● The problem with the above example is that such tests do not readily yield to technique, and to a certain extent you will arrive at the answer through trial-and-error. However, the presence of an odd number in the third series of numbers indicates that multiplication is necessary at some point in the calculation. Try multiplying the triangles: the answers are all even numbers and all larger than the circle. Therefore, to obtain the circle, there must then be a division. Dividing by the number in the square gives half the result, so divide by half the number in the square and you will arrive at your solution. However, the danger with all complex trial-and-error exercises is that you get flustered and start running around in circles.

All supervised tests are almost as much of a psychological as an intellectual challenge. If you get an attack of the shakes, it is best to relax, think of something else – the mortality of the ladybird – and then try again. If this does not help, move to the next question.

● Some tests in the numerical section can be verbal in disguise.
For example:

     1586   (1631)   3521

     8432   (....)   5289

Solution 8259.

● The above answer should not have been too difficult to find. However, some tests along these lines can be more difficult, involving arithmetical operations, such as those used for BT35 on page 31. For example, look at:

     2569   (1183)   1386

     7242   (....)   5321

Solution 1921.

(Deduct the right side from the left side.)

● Or, instead of adding or deducting numbers, add or subtract the sum of the digits on each side:

1234 (36) 5678

2345 (..) 6789

Solution 44.

(Add all the digits together.)

● Number squares, such at BT36 on page 31 will invariably involve arithmetical operations. These are mainly additions and subtractions, less frequently divisions and multiplications, and a combination of two operations is often used. Solving these completion problems is largely based on trial-and-error, so the best route towards a techniques is by several examples.

6	17	11
5	14	9
?	11	8

Solution 3.

(Deduct the left digit from the middle number to give the right digit.)

● Here is a more difficult problem:

2	6	3	4
2	8	4	4
3	5	?	5

Solution 3.

(Multiply the figures in the first two columns, and divide the product by the digit in the third column to give the number in the fourth column.)

● Another form of completion are number wheels where you need to fill in the missing segment. Look again at BT37 and BT39:

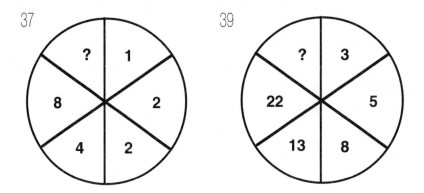

Admittedly these are again trial-and-error exercises, but even so you can be systematic about them. First try sums of opposites, or work your way around the wheel looking at ascending or descending differences and products. If none of these yield a result, try adding or subtracting the same number or going up or down. Thus:

37 1 x 2 = 2, 2 x 2 = 4, 2 x 4 = 8, 4 x 8 = 32

39 2 x 3- 1 = 5, 2 x 5 - 2 = 8, 2 x 8 - 3 = 13,
　　2 x 13 - 4= 22, 2 x 22 - 5 = 39

● A more difficult problem is represented by BT40.

10		1		15		3		12		2
	8				49				?	
8		3		8		4		6		4

Study it carefully with a view to finding a short–cut. The first figure offers no ready clue. However the second does. No additions and no subtractions will give 49. Division is equally unlikely as the lowest would be 98 divided by 2, and there is no reasonable way to arrive at 2. So look at multiplication. The only integers resulting in 49 (on multiplication) are 7 x 7. Add the sum of the right squares and multiply by the difference of the left squares and hey presto!

VISUO-SPATIAL

This group covers a range similar to verbal and numerical tests but, as the name implies, poses the question in optical images instead of words or numbers.

Selection

● As an example of selection tests, look at the one below.
Select the correct figure from the six numbered ones so that it belongs logically in the empty square.

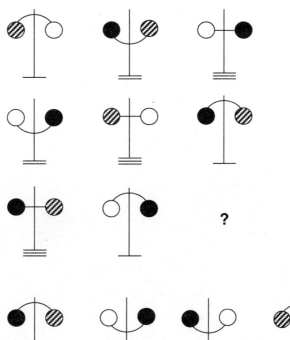

1   2   3   4   5   6

If systematically approached, this test can be solved easily and quickly. First look to see what each figure consists of:

1 The base has either one, two or three horizontal lines.

2 The cross-bar is either straight, bent upwards or bent downwards.

3 The circles are either black+white, black+shaded or white+shaded.

Now all you must do is find which features are missing in the last line. First notice that the two-line base is missing, so the answer is either 2 or 5. Then see that the white+shaded circles are needed, which identifies number 2 as the correct figure. You will notice that the third feature, the cross-bar, is not even needed for identification, although number 2 meets the requirement.

● Now try the following, using the same procedure:

Solution 6.

(A triangle is missing, so the answer is either 2, 4 or 6. A 'C' is missing, eliminating 4. The black triangle is needed, identifying number 6 as the solution.)

● Here is another test for you to solve using the same technique:

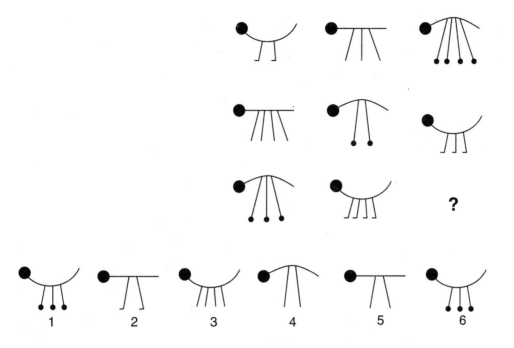

Solution 5.

(Using the same steps as before, a straight body is missing, so 2 and 5 would qualify. However, legs without shoes are missing, leaving 5. A double check by counting the number of legs leaves you in no doubt.)

● Some selection tests are more complex. For example, identify the correct figure from the six numbered ones to replace the question mark.

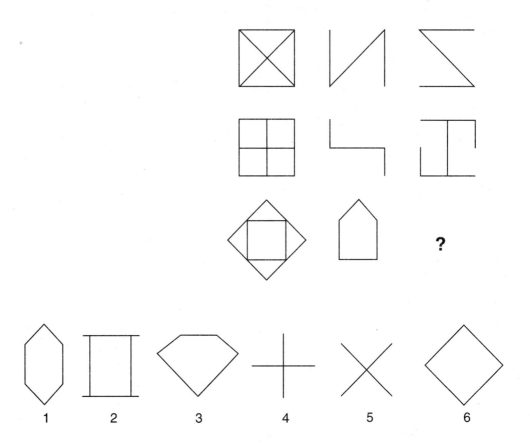

Solution 3.

(This follows a different principle from previous tests. The lines of the drawings in the second column are taken away from the first column to leave the third column. In other words, superimposing the second and third columns gives the figure in the first column.)

● A third type of selection test follows an entirely different line. Which belongs in the empty space?

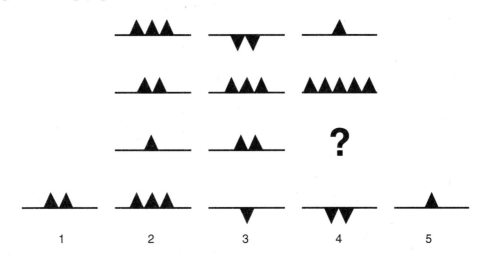

Solution 2.

(Each triangle over the line counts as +1, and each below –1.)

● There is no easy way to recognise visuo-spatial tests like the one above which are arithmetical in disguise. The symbols differ in numbers rather than in design, and are placed in two distinct locations, either above or below a line (see BT46 on page 35) or inside/outside a geometrical figure. Another alternative is shown in BT48 on page 36, which uses different symbols (male and female) instead of locations.

● Here is another example, this time with different symbols instead of locations to denote plus and minus:

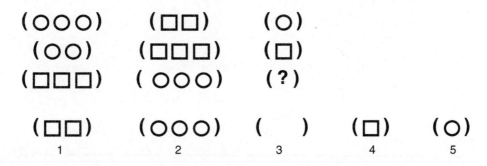

Solution 3.

(The circle stands for plus and the square stands for minus.
Therefore the last line reads –3 +3, and the answer is zero.)

● By now you will have gained enough experience to deal with most visuo-spatial selection tests. There are, however, some that contain a twist likely to baffle you unless you are well prepared. Here are two such examples.

Select the figure in the second row which would logically replace the question mark.

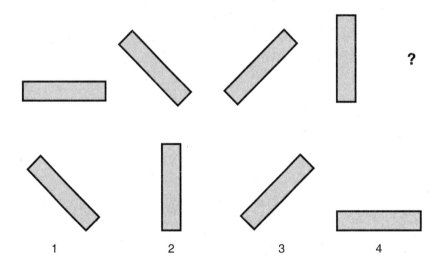

1   2   3   4

Solution 2.

(The rectangle turns clockwise with an increment of 45° each time, ie 45°, 90°, 135° and 180°.)

● Select the figure in the second row whiuch would logically replace the question mark.

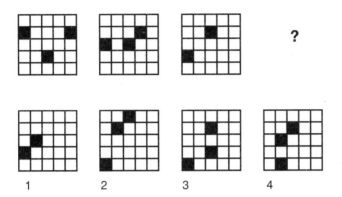

Solution 2.

(The black square in the first column moves each time one square down, in the third column one square up, and in the fifth column one square to the left. The fact that two black squares fuse into one as in figure 1 can give rise to confusion.)

● All these visuo-spatial examples are perfectly legitimate in their variety. However, there are some authors who specialise and excel in devising tests which are as difficult to break as a war-time code. Don't worry about them, they are not appropriate for a valid IQ test. Here is an example:

Find the appropriate numbered figure to fill the empty space in the top row.

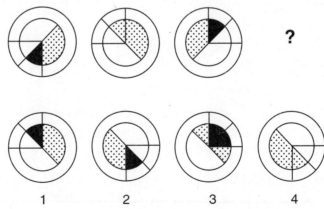

Solution 4.

(The two conjoined sectors of the outer circle rotate clockwise, and the dotted sector of the inner ring, rotates counter-clockwise. Whenever the black sector is outside the dotted sector, it disappears. Forget it! It is easier to construct obscure tests than to solve them.)

Odd man (or men) out

BT53 to BT56 on pages 38 to 39 are examples of finding the odd man out. These can be confusing and time-consuming. You will probably turn the figures around in your mind's eye to see which are congruent and which are not, and quite possibly you will try several times. There is, however, a very simple method which will provide a solution in seconds. For instance, take BT54 which could represent a cap and find the three odd men out.

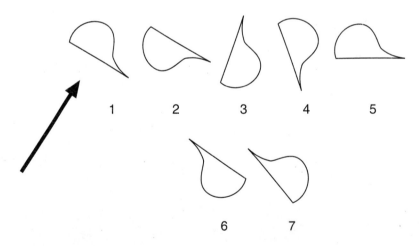

Solution 2, 3 and 7.

(Look at the base and just establish whether, viewed from the straight line as indicated by the arrow, the peak points right or left. Numbers 2, 3 and 7 point to the left. The same principle applies to all tests of this type.)

● A useful refinement for such a test is to jot down left (L) and right (R) as you proceed from 1 to 7. In this case, the notation would read:

1	2	3	4	5	6	7
R	L	L	R	R	R	L

Symmetry

● Test questions that involve symmetry can fall into any of the visuo-spatial categories. For example, among the odd man out questions, symmetry is the answer to BT52 on page 38. Likewise, BT51 on page 37 is similar, as turning the figures around is the key. Be on your guard for such questions where there is apparently no odd man out and look for symmetry or reversibility (upside down). In some cases, when nothing else seems to make sense, it is worth checking whether adding up the symbols either horizontally or vertically provides the answer, such as in BT42 (a selection question) and BT57 (an analogy) on pages 33 and 40.

Chapter Six

THE AFTER TEST

General directions

- You have 100 minutes to complete the 120 questions.

- Answer the questions as carefully and as quickly as you can.

- Begin at the beginning and go straight through.

- Don't give up easily, but if you have no clue move to the next question. You can always go back if you have time to spare.

- It is advisable to write your answers on a separate piece of paper so that the book can be used again.

- If you think you might have the right answer, note it down even if you are not quite certain.

- Do not exceed the time limit.

AFTER TEST QUESTIONS

VERBAL

Elimination

Underline the two words that do not belong with the others:

1 Knife, axe, needle, scissors, lance.

2 Reasoning, aptitude, knowledge, talent, experience.

3 Philosophy, geology, physics, physiology, psychology.

4 Receptionist, cobbler, blacksmith, tailor, consultant.

5 Glue, razor, nail, string, knife.

Find the odd man out:

6 Puma, leopard, bear, tiger, lion.

Find the odd man out:

7 Wolf, giraffe, deer, crocodile, zebra.

8 Investigated, listened, looked, heard, tested.

9 Stupid, ignorant, dim, brainless, dense.

10 Contradict, oppose, negate, deny, disprove.

Analogies

In each analogy below, the third and fourth words are missing, and you have to select from the group of words on the right the missing words. On each line, underline the two words needed to complete the analogy (not necessarily in the right order).

11 Second is to time   ... ounce, return, minute, weight.

12 Prediction is to future ... past, absence, memory, present.

13 Clumsy is to astute ... ugly, clever, awkward, stupid.

14 Hook is to eye ... flange, nut, screw, nail.

15 Dynamic is to static ... politic, active, effective, inert.

On each line below, the words run in pairs. Insert the missing word at the end of each line to complete the series.
Example: No - Never / Perhaps - Sometimes / Yes - (Always)

16 Line – Two / Square – Four / Pentagon – (............)

17 General – Generalise / Familiar – Familiarise/ Obedient – (............)

18 Memory – Memorise / Courage – Encourage / Joy – (............)

19 Analysis – Analyse / Agreement – Agree / Danger – (............)

20 Division – Divide / Amendment – Amend / Partition – (............)

Identify the word that will complete the analogy:

21 Revel is to lever as reward is to:
painter   drawer   sketcher   printer   writer

22 Abstract is to concrete as mind is to:
substance   fact   matter   mass   existence

23 Knowing is to believing as science is to:
philosophy   art   religion   psychology   fatalism

24 Lend is to borrow as harmony is to:

division   dispute   argument   doubt   discord

Antonyms

Underline in each row the word that is most nearly the opposite in meaning to the given word.

25 Exclude is the opposite of
(admit, count, receive, register, allow).

26 Approach is the opposite of
(distant, depart, leave, diminish, recede).

27 Limited is the opposite of
(unbounded, uncontrolled, free, liberal, unregulated).

28 Hurt is the opposite of
(restore, heal, atone, help, benefit).

29 Disagree is the opposite of
(match, settle, concur, consent, accede).

Find the word that fits

30 Find the word in the second line that will fit best into the
first line:

Condition War Caution Date Face

Clever Ignorant Mature Feeble Sane

Missing word

Insert the four-letter word missing in the lower brackets:

31 CINEMA   (NEAT)   THEATRE

   SOLENT   (. . . .)   STRANDS

32 ORBIT   (RILE)   WHEEL

   ARSON   (. . . .)   STEMS

33 ETHYL   (HERO)   FROWN

   UNTIL   (. . . .)   ABEAM

34 LOVER   (OVER)   READER

   TRIED   (. . . .)   ESTATE

Insert the four-letter word missing in the lower brackets:

35 CROSS   (SORE)   RENTS

     MAKES   (. . . .)   INLET

Alphabet problems

Using this letter square, answer the following questions:

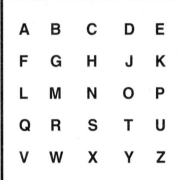

36 Find the letter that comes just above the letter just after S.

37 Find the letter that comes just before the letter above the letter which is above the letter between the letters S and U.

38 Find the letter that comes just below the letter just before the letter just above the letter which is midway between the letters F and K.

39 Find the letter that comes between the letter just below R and the letter just above T.

40 Find the letter that comes just above the letter that comes just before the letter just below P.

Identification

41 Insert the letter X above or below the line.

E   W   M   S
———————————————
O   H   I

NUMERICAL

Series

Insert the missing numbers.

42 1   1   2   4   8   ?

43 1   3   2   5   4   8   ?

44 ?   6   11   16   21

45 5   8   7   10   ?   12

46 3   12   5   10   7   ?   ?   6   11   4

47 4   81   8   27   ?   9   32   ?

Insert the missing numbers.

48

5	6	7	8	9
50	72	98	128	?

49

1	3	5	7	?
11	7	4	2	?

50

1	2	4	8	?
1	4	9	16	?

51

3	4	6	9	?
0	5	11	18	?

Insert the missing numbers.

52 1   4   9   16   ?

53 2   5   10   ?   26

Insert the missing numbers.

54 1   8   27   ?   125   216

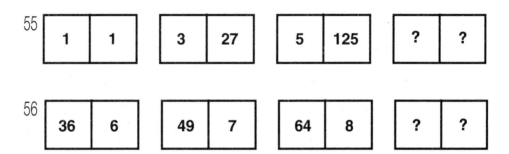

55

| 1 | 1 | | 3 | 27 | | 5 | 125 | | ? | ? |

56

| 36 | 6 | | 49 | 7 | | 64 | 8 | | ? | ? |

Analogies

57 If 6 = 4, how much is 9?

58 If ³/₄ = 5, how much is 6?

59 If 1³/₄ = 7, what is 8?

60 if -3 = 4, what is 9?

Completion

Each set of illustrations follows rules that will enable you to find the missing number.

Example:

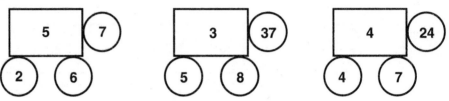

Multiply the wheels and deduct the cart

Insert the missing numbers.

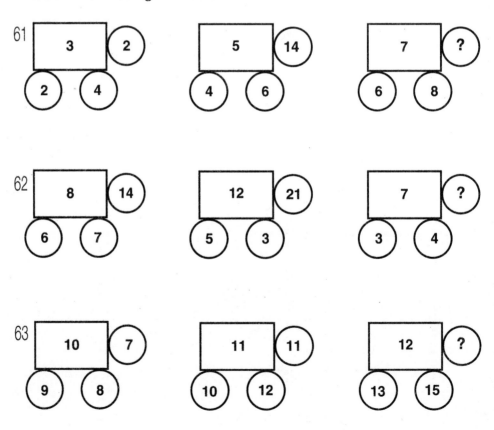

64

7	6	3
8	?	11
15	10	14

65

3	2	4
4	3	5
5	4	?

66

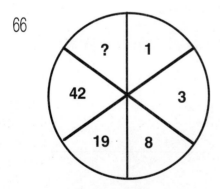

67

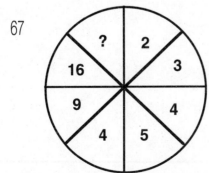

68 Insert the missing number.

6	7	8	9
7	8	9	?
8	9	0	1
9	0	1	2

Insert the missing number following the same principle as applied in the top row:

69 91425   (1275)   47352

    43821   (. . . .)   54713

70 384   (21)   213

    731   (. .)   581

71 45937   (5739)   78293

    81362   (. . . .)   43279

Insert the missing number.

72

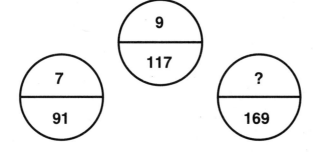

73

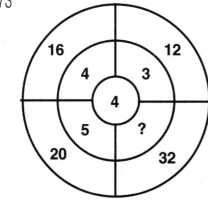

74

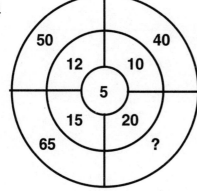

Insert the missing numbers.

75

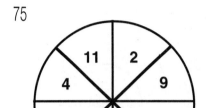

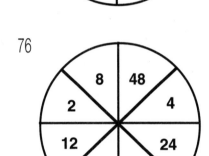

76

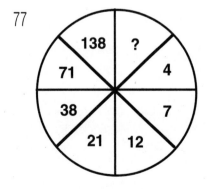

77

Odd man out

Find the odd man out.

78 18   27   45
    15   24   32

79 49   21   35
    77   84   65

80 46   37   52
    91   64   82

VISUO-SPATIAL

Selection

81 Select the correct figure from the five numbered ones.

MMM	N	MM		
N	MM	M		
M	NN	?		

MM	NN	N	NNN	M
1	2	3	4	5

82 Select the correct figure from the five numbered ones.

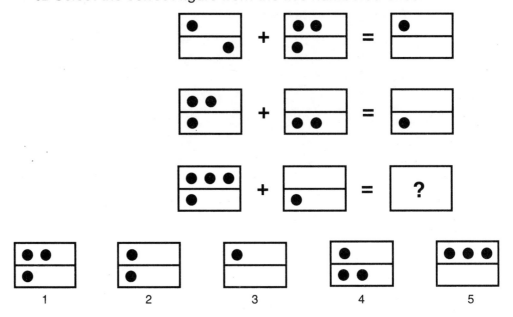

83 Select the correct figure from the five numbered ones.

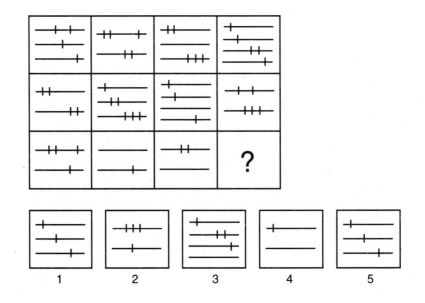

84 Select the correct figure from the six numbered ones.

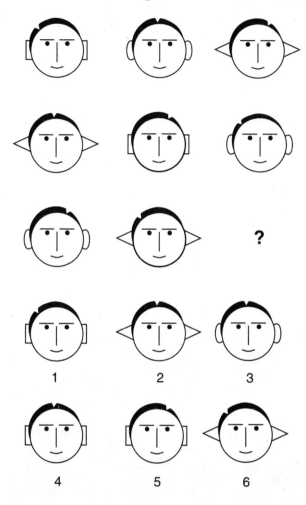

85 Select the correct figure from the five numbered ones.

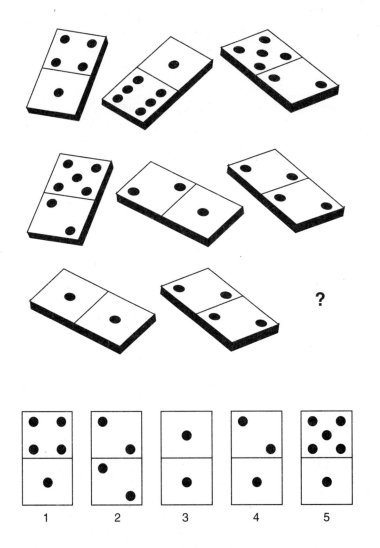

86 Select the correct figure from the six numbered ones.

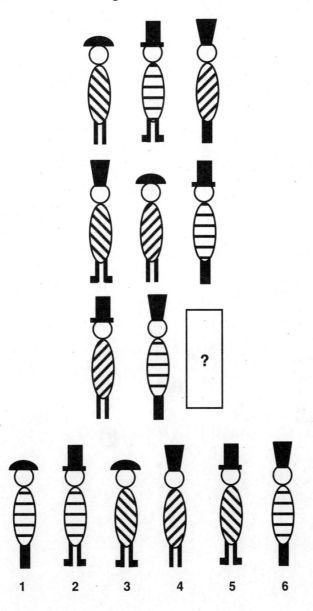

87 Select the correct figure from the six numbered ones.

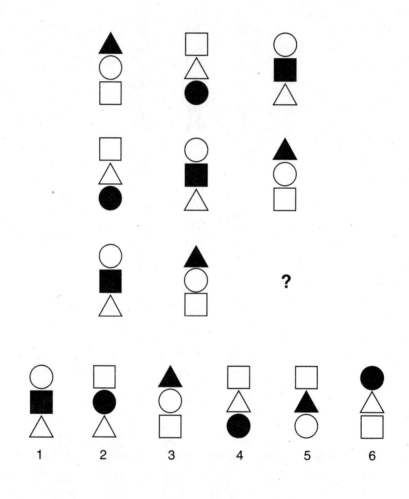

88 Select the correct figure from the six numbered ones.

    ?

   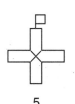

1   2   3   4   5   6

89 Select the correct figure from the six numbered ones.

    ?

1   2   3   4   5   6

90 Select the correct figure from the five numbered ones that follows the same rule which applies to the letters on the left.

1   2   3   4   5

91 Select the correct figure from the five numbered ones.

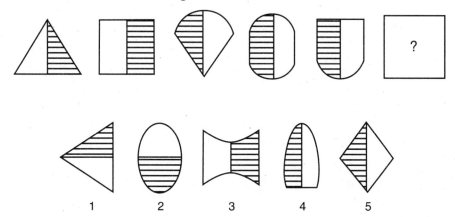

1   2   3   4   5

92 Select the correct figure from the five numbered ones.

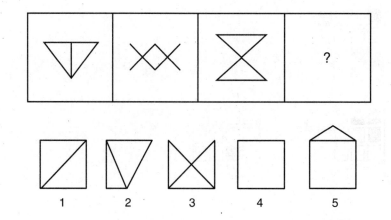

1   2   3   4   5

93 Select the correct figure from
the six numbered ones.

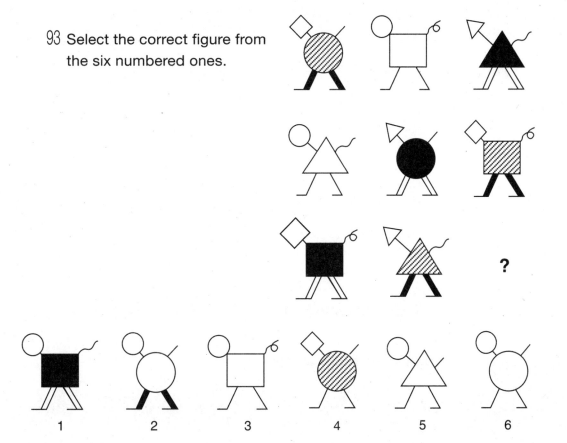

94 Select the correct figure from the three numbered ones.

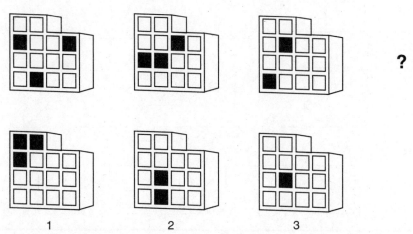

95 Select the correct figure from the four numbered ones.

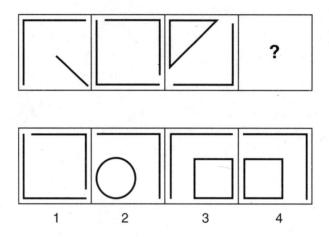

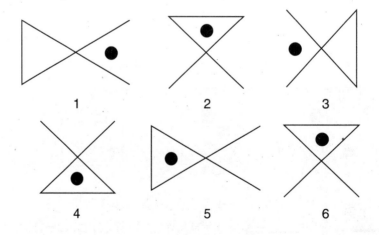

Odd man out

96 Find the odd man out.

97 Find the odd man
out.

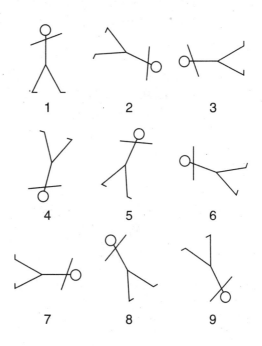

98 In the line below identify the two shapes which, without
turning over, could cover each other:

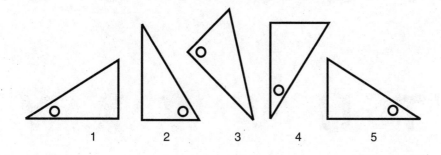

In each line below identify the two pairs which, without
turning over, could cover each other:

99

1   2   3   4   5   6

100

1   2   3   4   5

Find the odd man out (visually)

101 **A   B   C   D   E   F**

102 **1   2   3   4   5   6   7**

103 **T   U   V   W   X   Y**

104 Find the odd man out

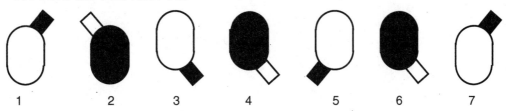

1   2   3   4   5   6   7

105 Find the two odd men out.

1   2   3   4   5   6

106 Find the three odd
men out.

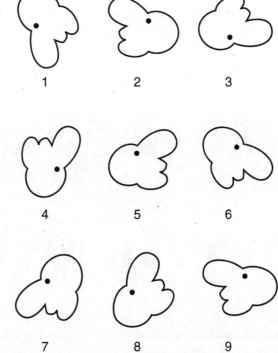

1   2   3

4   5   6

7   8   9

107 Find the three odd men out.

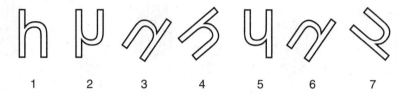

1 2 3 4 5 6 7

108 Find the odd man out (which cannot be paired with any other figure).

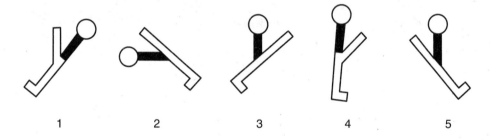

1 2 3 4 5

109 Find the odd man out.

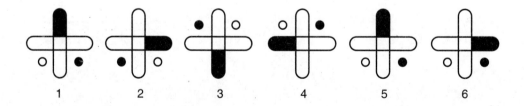

1 2 3 4 5 6

Analogies

110 Select the correct figure from the four numbered ones,
turning them around but not over.

F is to ∃ as T is to: ⌐ ⌐ I ⌐

                     1   2   3   4

111 Select the correct figure from the five numbered ones,
turning them around but not over.

B is to ⮝ as ⮝ is to:

       1   2   3   4   5

112 Select the correct figure from the four numbered ones.

LLS is to SSL as 116 is to:

661 611 161 616

  1   2   3   4

113 Select the correct figure from the six numbered ones.

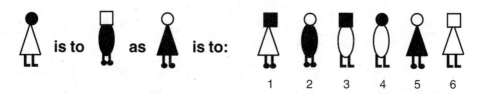

1   2   3   4   5   6

Series

The shapes on the left-hand side form a pattern. Select the numbered shape on the right-hand side that continues the pattern.

114

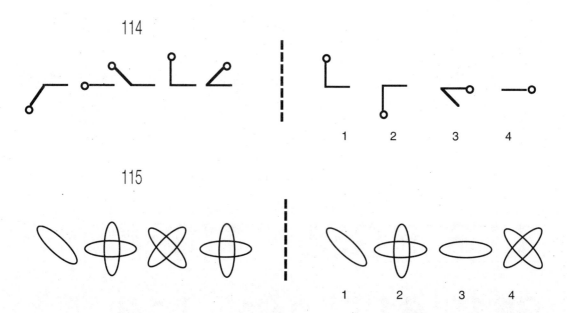

115

116

117

118

119

120

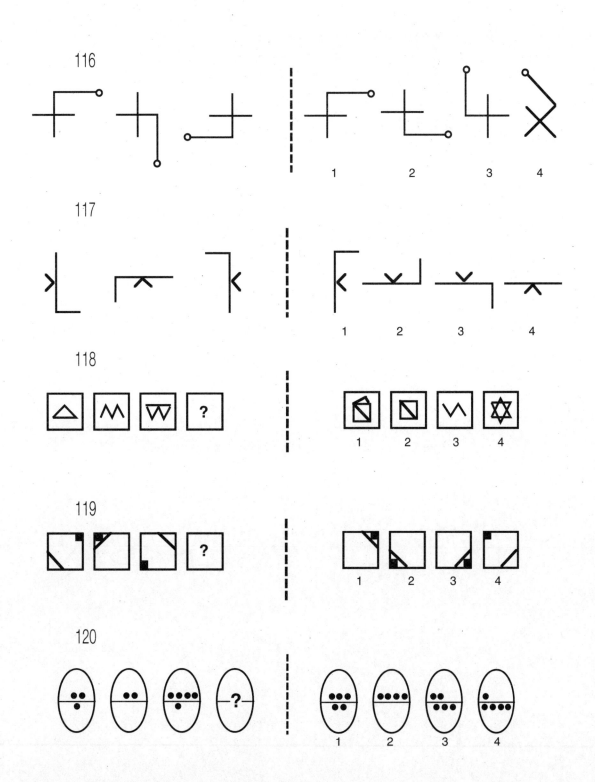

AFTER TEST ANSWERS

1 Needle, lance.
   (They pierce, the others cut.)

2 Knowledge, experience.
   (These are acquired, the others have a genetic element.)

3 Philosophy, psychology.
   (Dealing with the mind, the others dealing with matter.)

4 Receptionist, consultant.
   (Dealing with people, the others with things.)

5 Razor, knife.
   (Cut, the others fix.)

6 Bear.
   (The others are cats.)

7 Crocodile.
(A water dweller.)

8 Heard.
(Passive, the others are active.)

9 Ignorant.
(Lack of knowledge, no genetic deficiency.)

10 Disprove.
(To prove incorrect constructively, the others are just negative.)

11 Ounce, weight.

12 Past, memory.

13 Clever, stupid.

14 Screw, nut.

15 Active, inert.

16 Five.

17 Obey.

18 Enjoy.

19 Endanger.

20 Partition.

21 Drawer.
(Drawer is reward back-to-front, as is revel and lever.)

22 Matter.

23 Religion.

24 Discord.

25 Admit.

26 Recede.
(Depart and leave imply a stationary condition before movement takes place, which recede does not.)

27 Unbounded.

28 Heal.

29 Concur.
(Consent and accede come close but they are more in the nature of acquiescing than positively agreeing.)

30 Mature.
(All the words in the top row can be prefixed with pre- to give another word: premature.)

31 Lean.

32 Rose.

33 Tube.

34 Rise or rite, both qualify.

35 Skin.

36 O.

37 H.

38 G.

39 S.

40 O.

41 Below the line.
(All letters below the line are symmetrical about a horizontal and vertical axis.)

42 16.
(The sum of all preceding numbers.)

43 7.
(Consecutive numbers add 2, deduct 1, add 3, deduct 1, add 4, etc.)

44 1.
(Difference between numbers is 5.)

45 9.
(Add 3, deduct 1.)

46 8, 9.

(There are two series thus: 3, 5, 7, 9, 11 and 12, 10, 8, 6, 4.)

47 16, 3.

(Again, two series: 4, 8, 16, 32 and 81, 27, 9, 3.)

48 162.

(Each top number is squared and doubled.)

49
13
26

(Top row increases by 1, 2, 3, 4. Bottom row by 5, 6, 7, 8.)

50
9
1

(Top row is a series of odd numbers. Bottom row is a descending series deducting 4, 3, 2, 1.)

51
16
25

(Top row doubles preceding number. Bottom row squares 1, 2, 3, 4, 5.)

52 25.

(Squares of the numbers 1, 2, 3, 4, 5.)

53 17.

(The same numbers as above adding 1.)

54 64.

(The cubes of 1, 2, 3, 4, 5 and 6.)

55 343.

(The left-hand side is a series of odd numbers, the right-hand side is their cubes.)

56 81, 9.

(The left-hand side are the squares of the right-hand side.)

57 6.

(9 is $1^1/_2$ times 6, and 6 is $1^1/_2$ times 4.)

58 40.

(6 is $^{24}/_4$, i.e. 8 times $^3/_4$, therefore 5 becomes 40.)

59 32.

60 -12.

61 34.

(Multiply the cart by the left wheel and deduct the right wheel.)

62 16.

(Cart less left wheel, multiplied by right wheel.)

63 16.

(Add wheels and deduct cart.)

64 4.

(Add the first two numbers in each column, giving the third.)

65 6.

(Horizontally, deduct first 1 and then add 2.)

66 89.

(Double each number and add 1, 2, 3, 4, 5.)

67 25.

(Each number is squared in the opposite field.)

68 0.

(The numbers are used in the order of 6 7 8 9 0 1 2, each line beginning with the second number in the line before.)

69 3241.

(These digits are in the same position as 1275 is in the top line.)

70 25.

(Sum of the digits.)

71 1279.

(In the same position as 5739.)

72 13.

(The larger number is 13 times the smaller.)

73 8.

(Starting with the centre 4, multiply with the number in the middle circle to give the number in the outer circle.)

74 90.

(Multiply 5 with the number in the middle circle and deduct 10.)

75 8.

(Opposite numbers add up to 17.)

76 1.

(The product of opposite numbers is 48.)

77 270.

(Clockwise, starting with 4, double and deduct 1, 2, 3, 4, 5, 6.)

78 32.

(All the others are divisible by 3.)

79 65.

(All the others are divisible by 7.)

80 52.

(The two digits of all the other numbers add up to 10.)

81 3.

(Each M stands for +1 and each N for -1. The last column
represents the sum.)

82 3.

(Each dot above the line represents +1, below the line -1.)

83 4.

(The total number of lines and crosslines in each column add up to
19.)

84 4.

(Ears are either square, round or triangular, and the parting is
either right, left or centre. An example of each occurs only once
in any row or column.)

85 4.

(In each column the numbers add up to 14.)

86 3.

(The only figure combining the missing hat, body and legs.)

87 4.

(There are circles, squares and triangles in each of the three positions; one is black, the others white.)

88 5.

(There are three main figures, three small ones inside the main ones, and three positions of the flag.)

89 1.

(There are three types of arms: nought, one or two; three types of shoe: nought, square or round; and three different positions.)

90 5.

(Straight letters are blackened south, curved letters north, letters with straight and curved lines are blackened west.)

91 4.

(All figures containing a curve are shaded west, all others are shaded east.)

92 4.

(It has four straight lines, like all figures in the top row.)

93 6.

(In each row and column there are three kinds of body [round, square and triangular], three types of head [also round, square and triangular], three types of leg [line, black and white]. In addition, the bodies are either white, black or shaded. The missing chicken must therefore be as number 6.)

94 1.

(The black window in the far left column goes down one square each time before it starts again at the top; the black window in the second column goes up one square each time; the black window in the second horizontal row from the top moves left one square each time.)

95 4.

(The right angle is moving counter-clockwise. The changing figure increases the number of its line segments by one in each succeeding square.)

96 5.

(The structures turn clockwise 90° at a time. The dot moves anticlockwise from quarter field to quarter field.)

97 7.

(All the other figures can be superimposed upon each other.)

98 4, 5.

99 2, 4 and 1, 6.

100 2, 4 and 3, 5.

101 F.
(All other letters are symmetrical about a horizontal or vertical axis.)

102 3.
(The only digit which is horizontally symmetrical.)

103 X.
(The only letter which is symmetrical about both axes.)

104 3.
(All black bodies can be rotated into each other. So can all white bodies, except 3.)

105 3, 4.
(All others can be rotated into each other.)

106 5, 6, 8.
(All others can be rotated into each other.)

107 1, 4, 5.

(These three cannot be rotated into any of the other four.)

108 3.

(2 and 5, as well as 1 and 4, can be rotated to form mirror images.)

109 6.

(The black arm and black spot rotate clockwise, the white spot counter-clockwise.)

110 3.

(T is turned 180° and a crossbar is added.)

111 5.

(The figure is turned anti-clockwise 135°.)

112 1.

(The last figure and number are duplicated and set in front.)

113 3.

(A white triangle turns into a black oval and therefore a black triangle turns into a white oval. The same changeover applies to the heads and feet.)

114 4.

(The line with the head rotates clockwise at 45°.)

115 1.

(The two ellipses cover each other in the first figure. One ellipse rotates clockwise by 45° and the other also 45° but counter-clockwise.)

116 3.

(The headed line rotates clockwise by 90°, the other line also 90° but counter-clockwise.)

117 2.

(The footed line rotates clockwise by 90°, the arms counter-clockwise by 90°.)

118 4.

(The number of lines in the figure increases by one each time.)

119 3.

(The inner triangle moves clockwise. The square moves counter-clockwise.)

120 2.

(Dots above the line are plus, below the line are minus. So the series is: 1, 2, 3, 4.)

HOW TO SCORE

For each correct answer to the After Test score one point. To find your rating, use the diagram below and proceed as you did for the Before Test (see page 51). The measure of the advantage you have gained through test sophistication is the difference in IQ points between the Before Test and After Test results.

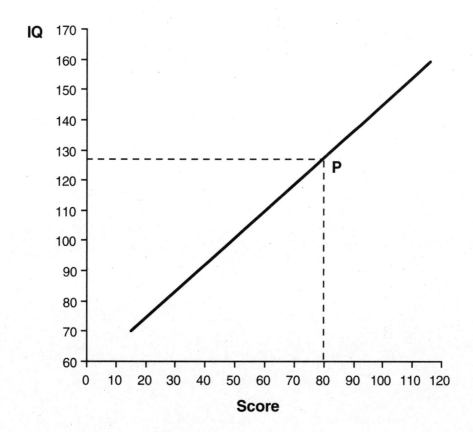

How Did You Get On ?

Dear Reader

Your response will be much appreciated. Not only will it provide important statistical information, but you will also participate in a monthly prize draw, offering books signed by the author.

First Prize   **JOURNEY THROUGH PUZZLELAND**
             and **LATERAL LOGIC PUZZLES**

Second prize   **JOURNEY THROUGH PUZZLELAND**

There will be 12 draws in total, one on the 1st of each month, starting on 1st July 1996.

Your reply will be entered in each draw until 1st June 1997. Winning replies will not be re-entered for the draw.

Cut here

- -

Name .... Age .... Date ....

Address ....

....

....

Tel No .... Fax No ....

Ocupation ....

Where did you obtain this book? ....

Before Test score .... After Test score ....

How would you classify The IQ Booster on a scale of 1 (exellent) to 5 (not useful)?

.... 1 .... 2 .... 3 .... 4 .... 5 ....

Other comments ....

....

Comtrade Limited

FREEPOST

86 North Gate

Prince Albert Road

London

NW8 7EJ